Praise For
"THE LION WHO FLINCHED"

"The Lion Who Flinched is an engrossing and thought-provoking tale of living productively, considerately, and creatively with others. Selter paints a gentle yet dynamic picture of young Barrabou, the heir apparent in the lion pride, who, through a series of adventures, becomes ready to lead his own pride. In the process, he discovers essential principles for leading and getting along with others with harmony and cooperation. Barrabou's lessons, which he enunciates clearly, are for all of us. Young people on the threshold of adulthood will find Barrabou's metaphoric story especially inspiring and his lessons a model for a fulfilling, impactful, and contributing life."

Noelle Sterne, PhD, Essayist, Novelist, Poet, Mainstream and Academic Editor

"Jed Selter's story of Barrabou in The Lion Who Flinched tells of a young lion coming of age, his challenges, and successes. Throughout the story, I reflected on lessons taught my sons by our family about love, respect, and courage to stand up for your beliefs, just like Barrabou was taught. In Barrabou's journey, empathy and honesty were at the core of his relationships, life lessons that will serve him well as he begins his new pride."

Sheila Walters, B.A. Education/M.A. Counseling, Retired High School Counsel/Dept. Head

"Jed Selter has created a thoughtful book that can be a valuable tool in fostering positive interpersonal relationships among children and pre-teens. The lessons the lion cub learns are valuable life lessons for all of us and the helpful discussion guide provides a tool in sharing that knowledge with youth. Scout leaders, advisers to youth leaders, teachers, and others who have regular contacts with young people should consider using this book in a group setting."

Susan Syrcle, B.A., Psychology/Sociology, B.A., Elementary Education, M.S. in Education

"Like many, I have witnessed and experienced the two basic leadership styles - top-down, command-and-control versus the more participative and team-oriented approach. In this book, you see through the eyes of the lion cub, Barrabou, as he observes then compares and contrasts the two styles. Gently and thoughtfully, the author manages to capture a broad spectrum of life experiences for which the lessons apply—from children at play to adults in workplace teams."

Gaston Peter-Contesse, CPA, MBA, CFO of Kitsap Physical Therapy & Sports Clinics

"This book has managed to bring me back to my childhood soul as an ever-learning human being, husband, father, and friend. Jed has given me life lessons to ponder, practice, and file for whenever I need them to remind me of what is truly important as I "grow up." If I had read this book in my younger years, it would have helped me understand life around me better and guide me through the difficult times I experienced...that we all do and will. I highly recommend this simple "life story" and its messages for anyone still looking for an "ah-ha" moment of clarity and understanding." It is an excellent primer for young people to consider and beneficial for adults' personal and business relationships."

Tim Meuret, Facilities and I.T. Project Manager (Ret.), Boeing

"In reading this book, I found myself in a new place as a grandfather wanting to talk with my grandkids or have them read this and then talk with them about it. That's a new place for me. I have been blessed with a few people in my life who hold up life in a unique fashion and take the time to document experiences in a way that creates passion and direction towards the "Greater Good." It's a purposeful life goal of my dear friend Jed Selter to weave the fabric, to tell the stories as a tribal elder should for all to appreciate. This book is one more chapter in his life to love."

Dennis M. Broughton, Exec. Director (Ret.), Boeing; Owner, Fusion Strategies Consulting

"I loved your story! The Lion Who Flinched is a modern Aesop fable. The flow was easy reading and had a touch of adventure, romance, and thought-provoking lessons. I think it is politically good timing as many of us are suffering from finding ways to communicate better with our families, friends, and acquaintances who have opposite views on political philosophies."

Carol Collins, Former 6th Grade Teacher

The Lion Who Flinched

The Cub Who Would Be King

Jed Selter

KITSAP
PUBLISHING

The Lion Who Flinched
First edition, published 2021

By Jed Selter
Illustrations by Abby Stoffel

Paperback ISBN-13: 978-1-952685-32-3
Hardbound ISBN-13: 978-1-952685-35-4

202108
150-10 9 8 7 6 5 4 3 2 1

Published by Kitsap Publishing
P.O. Box 572
Poulsbo, WA 98370
www.KitsapPublishing.com

Acknowledgments

My sincere appreciation and thanks to several people who assisted in this project, including my wife, Darla, my sister, Noelle, my publisher Ingemar Anderson and several close friends who took the time to read and comment on the manuscript.

A special thank you to Abby Stoffel, who illustrated the book. Abby's incredibly sensitive interpretations in her colorful illustrations helped to make the story come alive.

Contents

Introduction

This book is about the basics to help live one's life more fully. It is about understanding "self," focusing on the Greater Good, and using tools to minimize anxiety.

Through the story of the growing awareness of Barrabou, a smaller than average male lion cub in the Gir Forest of India, the book invites us to consider how to manage ourselves; how to develop positive, long-lasting relationships; how to build and cement trust and respect with others; and how to lead effectively. Using the principles taught by his wise grandfather, Barrabou becomes a mature, compassionate, and strong young leader.

I have written this book to be beneficial for adults and adolescents. I hope that this will help people make conscious decisions about living fruitfully and being happier in conducting themselves.

Most chapters conclude with a "Spirit of the Lion Lesson," reiterating the chapter's central premise. In the Discussion Guide for Adults and Adolescents, each "Lesson" is followed by a brief "Introspection" worksheet for adults to use in applying the lessons themselves.

Each Introspection is followed by a "Dialogue with Cubs" worksheet to help adults engage with others about the subject of the chapter. With chapter worksheets as guides, teachers, parents, mentors, leaders, and others can initiate dialogues to internalize the tools to live their lives with grace and peace of mind.

Even without the Discussion Guide, the messages in the book are applicable in our daily lives and can help in how we manage ourselves and interact with each other.

No wild animals were harmed or domesticated in the writing of this book.

Jed Selter

PS: I will be donating a significant portion of the proceeds from book sales to nonprofits benefiting children.

Foreword

This book speaks to self and organizational management and leadership principles in a colorful and intriguing wildlife setting. It may help people become more aware of themselves for success in their personal lives and careers.

The book is dedicated to the strength and power of the human spirit.

With a focus beyond ourselves to do the Good we can do for all of us, our collective future is limitless in hope, love, and success for all humankind.

The book reflects principles developed and taught by the author, Jed Selter, through the former J.S. Associates, Inc, which he founded and managed.

Synopsis

Through observations in his father's pride, coaching from his grandfather, and introspections on life in the wild, a maturing lion cub learns the lessons of managing fear, understanding himself, relationships, respect for others, and servant leadership.

A discussion guide accompanies the story for adults and adolescents, which expands on the principles described in the story. Adults are led through a series of rhetorical questions and exercises in preparation for guided discussions with adolescents.

The target audience for the book is adolescents and adults.

Setting: In the Gir Forest

On the west coast of India along the Arabian Sea lies the Indian peninsular state of Gujarat. In the Saurashtra Peninsula of Gujarat lies Gir National Park. The Gir is a mixed deciduous forest with teak, flame of the forest, acacia, and banyan trees. It is hilly with many rivers. The park is approximately forty miles from Junagadh and twenty miles from Verawal.

The Forest is a one-hundred-sixteen-square-mile sanctuary created to protect the last wild population of lions outside Africa. The park is a haven for about three hundred Asiatic lions.

In the middle of the preserve lives one of the largest lion prides in India. Rantour, the King of the pride, and his lioness, Aleyma, have ruled and led this pride for many years.

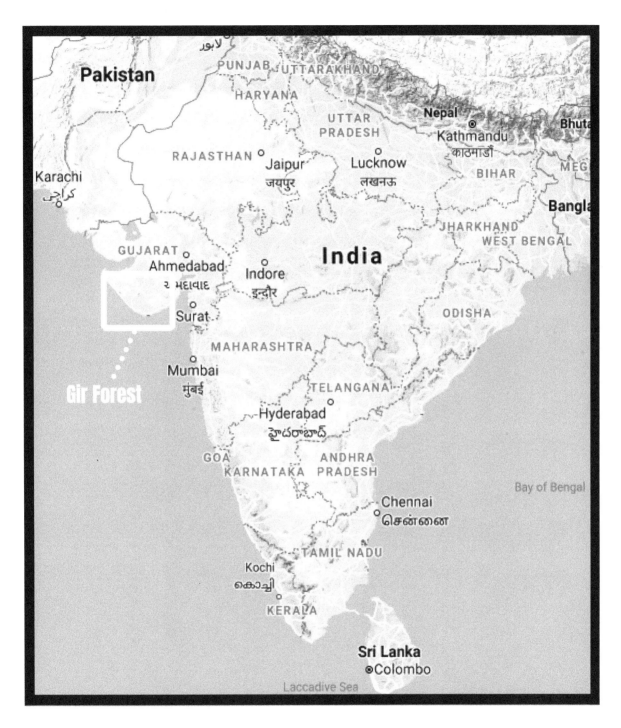

(Source: Google Maps)

Chapter One
First Look

Aleyma, getting up in years for bearing young, was pregnant with another cub. This cub would be Aleyma's fifth offspring. The previous four cubs were all healthy females.

Rantour and Aleyma were tremendously proud of their young lionesses. Even as adolescents, the girls had quickly picked up the art of stalking and hunting, and each in her own right had developed a reputation for being an exceptional hunter. Much of what they had learned was from Aleyma, so she was doubly proud of their progress and accomplishments.

If this cub is a girl, they would love her as they do their others, but a male would round out the family.

Although he never mentioned it to Aleyma, it was apparent that Rantour, as King of the pride, felt the pressure to have a male cub.

As well thought of and liked as their lioness cubs were, Rantour always heard the gossip among the other lions. He knew that they joked behind his back that their "mighty King" could not spawn a male heir.

Rantour felt the pressure to have a son whom he could show off in front of the other males in the pride. He also wanted to train and groom a young strapping male to be as fearsome as he was and would one day rule his lion pride as the ferocious king that Rantour was. So, as Aleyma's time neared, it was not without nervousness that Rantour awaited the birth.

Believing this cub to be Aleyma's last, Rantour's father, Morinour, who was king of another pride, traveled the fifty kilometers from his pride to witness the birth.

As she had for her previous four births, Aleyma could sense her time growing close. With just the slightest nod to Rantour, she slowly shuffled her way to the grassy hollow on the outskirts of the pride's village where she had delivered her other, now-youngster cubs.

Aleyma gently settled down into the soft grass with her back firmly braced against the large cool flat rock. Rantour and Morinour lay down facing her to watch over her and comfort her. They periodically brought Aleyma food and water and were ready to attend to her every need. They soothed her with quiet conversation and joked about the great things this little one would be known for in Indian lion lore.

After a day and a half wait, Aleyma seemed to be getting ready. Her contractions grew more robust and steady enough that she felt it would be any time now. She was right.

In the early morning of the second day, at the onset of sunrise, Aleyma gave birth, almost painlessly, to a cub in the morning dew. Rantour and Morinour watched, expecting that her last cub would be a fifth female. But, to their great joy, this cub was a male. Both lions pranced around, roaring at the top of their lungs, announcing to all that a male cub had been born to the king and his lioness.

The tiny newborn cub took a huge breath and exhaled with the first sigh of his new life. He squirmed and stretched in the grass to shake off his time in the womb and begin his journey into the world. The newborn cub opened his eyes for the first time, blinking hard several times. As the infant cub dozed off, Aleyma nuzzled the side of his face with great pride.

Rantour stood over him and softly licked his fur to a brilliant sheen. Morinour looked on with great pride at his lion king son and the new cub.

As Rantour and Morinour "inspected" this little fellow, they both felt excited to have a male cub to carry on their family lineage. But each of them registered concern for the newborn. They saw immediately that this cub was different from the other male cubs born in the pride. Smaller than average, he looked frailer than most male cubs.

It was obvious to both Rantour and Morinour that this one would take special caring for. Rantour looked at his newborn son closely and said to himself, "He is not a bad-looking cub. He has large bright eyes and seems intelligent like his sisters. But, since he is frailer than most, I will have to teach him to be the most ferocious of lions, so he can survive and control those around him to become king of his own pride someday. I will teach him how to strike fear in every other lion, as I do, so there is no doubt that he, too, is a king."

Morinour slowly circled the newborn. He looked closely at him and said to himself, "He is a handsome little fellow. He has large bright eyes and seems intelligent like his sisters. But since he is frailer than most, I will stay close to this little one and teach him how to be a leader among lions, to beckon others to follow him out of trust and respect. He will become a legendary lion king through graceful determination and caring for others."

And so, a new cub came to make his way into the Gir Forest. It was the continuation of the cycle of life in the wilderness played out for thousands of years.

Harkening back through four generations, they decided to name him for his forefathers. Revered for their wisdom as leaders, they were known as "Baras."

So, they named the cub Barrabou.

Although the adults didn't know it, this cub would change the ways of the lion.

Chapter Two
Awakening

While a cub, Barrabou stayed close to his mother. Nursing, he felt secure cuddling in the concaves of her warm, comforting body. He loved to doze, listening to her muffled heartbeat caressing his small frame as he fell asleep against her tummy.

As Barrabou grew and ventured out little by little away from Aleyma, he realized that he was somewhat alone. There were only a few cubs in the pride, and, including his sisters, most were much older than he.

Barrabou had no male cub peers to play with and learn from. Although he sometimes played with the older cubs, they easily dominated him. He felt uncomfortable, and they intimidated him. He rarely frolicked for long periods with the other cubs or went for long romps with them. They were older and did not want to be bothered by him. So Barrabou had to find ways to entertain himself.

He became a watcher. He got into the habit of stepping back and observing things. Later, he would sit quietly and play back in his head what he had seen and reflect on what he could learn from it. He could remember and play these short scenes for himself any time he liked. He made it his own private game to keep replaying the scenes and thinking deeply about them. He would play a scene in slow motion and then stop it, asking himself questions to see how much he had observed.

More and more, Barrabou began to enjoy playing this game in his head. The more he stayed by himself, the more distant he became from the other cubs. They sensed his desire to be alone and eventually ignored him and left him to himself—with one exception.

She was a cub about his age. Like Barrabou, she was bright and observant. She had a beautiful face with large sparkling brown eyes and a beckoning smile. The daughter of one of Aleyma's closest friends, her name was Lucindra, but everyone called her Lucy.

The two cubs quickly became close friends and confidants. Barrabou would tell Lucy about his observations and reflections, and they would sometimes discuss them at length. Lucy was a marvelous sounding board for Barrabou, asking him questions and helping him fully consider his thoughts and conclusions.

Although Rantour saw Barrabou with Lucy a lot, Rantour noticed Barrabou's reluctance to join the older cubs. Seeing Barrabou's isolation, Rantour started teaching Barrabou how to be a king earlier than he otherwise would have.

So Barrabou spent most of his waking hours with his father, the king, experiencing the daily life of the lion pride through Rantour's eyes. Barrabou continued to visualize what he observed with the other lions and their interactions with his father. And, he continued to talk with Lucy about what he saw.

As he grew older, Barrabou kept mental notes of what he observed, how he felt, and what he learned. He digested and revisited these ideas over and over in his mind's eye. They were so vivid for Barrabou that he began to organize them in his head as his private lessons in life—lessons he could live by.

As he formed these lessons, he would talk to Lucy about them. They would exchange thoughts for hours about the meaning of his observations and how to apply his ideas. Both Barrabou and Lucy took great joy in these talks and always looked forward to their next sessions.

Barrabou called this collection the Spirit of the Lion Lessons.

Chapter Three
Controlling Through Fear

Trailing his father's every footstep all day, Barrabou saw Rantour in two ways: as his father at home in the family den and as king interacting with the others in the pride. Very confused, Barrabou saw his father as two completely different personalities—the one at home he loved and the one feared by other lions.

When Rantour was with Aleyma and the family, he was warm and caring. He spoke softly and laughed with them. He played with them and treated them gently. When he scolded them, he did so with the softest of eyes and always caressed them afterward. Even then, Rantour's scoldings were mild. They were more like little lessons than actual scoldings.

But when Barrabou saw Rantour in the pride with the other lions, he was ferocious. He worked himself up and furrowed his brow in anger. He yelled and roared. He would crouch and spring at the others, often slapping them hard in the face with his open paw, claws extended. The other lions cowered in his presence. It seemed to Barrabou that Rantour purposely planned these outbursts and created this tension to keep the other lions off guard. He would nip at the other lions without provocation and with no warning, just to keep them off balance and afraid of him. It appeared to be Rantour's way of assuring that the others would submit to his demands.

It took Barrabou some time to muster the courage, but he finally asked his father about how he acted. Loping through the pride one day beside Rantour, Barrabou said, as casually as he could, "Father, I am confused by how you act." Trying to remain nonchalant, but fearing his father's reaction, Barrabou continued. "Why are you so angry and mean with the other lions when I know you to be so warm and loving at home?"

Rantour stopped in his tracks and turned to face Barrabou. Barrabou was instantly frightened. He stood motionless, facing his father.

In a soft but emphatic guttural whisper, Rantour commanded, "Barrabou, follow me to the cave at the edge of the village." With that, Rantour spun around and strode quickly west of the village to the cave. Barrabou followed his father as fast as he could.

When they arrived, Rantour motioned with his head for Barrabou to sit in the cave entrance. As Barrabou did so, Rantour stood directly over Barrabou in a position of absolute dominance. Rantour then arched his shoulders and bent down, so he was nose to nose with Barrabou. He stared at Barrabou with bared teeth and snorted loudly several times. He was so close that the moisture from his nostrils created a cold, wet blanket on Barrabou's muzzle. Barrabou feared for his very life.

He had to remind himself almost out loud that this was his loving father and that he would never hurt Barrabou.

Rantour spoke. "My son, someday you will be in my position. To be king, you will need to be fierce, as I am. To stay in power, you will always need to strike fear in others." Rantour paused and then continued. "If I were to do otherwise, the other lions would interpret it as weakness, and they would not respect me. I would no longer be King."

Barrabou sat motionless, shocked.

Rantour lowered his eyes to the ground, sighed, and fell silent. Then he slowly raised his head and again stared into Barrabou's eyes. In a low monotone voice, Rantour said, "Barrabou, you must never show vulnerability. Stare other lions down. Make them feel your wrath and your power. Make them back down and cower in your presence. You must never flinch. If you flinch, you will lose."

Barrabou was again struck dumb with fear. As much as he wanted to get up and run, he could not move a muscle. He couldn't respond or talk back or argue. The King had spoken. All the cub could say, trying to sound calm and strong, was, "Yes, father. Thank you, Sir."

Rantour growled a loud fearsome growl, scaring Barrabou even more. Then he wheeled around and walked away, leaving Barrabou trembling.

For days after this encounter with his father, Barrabou was skittish around Rantour. He had felt Rantour's wrath, and he was greatly troubled by it. Rantour acted as if nothing had happened, but Barrabou kept his distance.

Barrabou played the "encounter at the cave," as he called it, repeatedly in his head. He thought about how his father had acted and what he had said. Barrabou thought about his feelings and how he had reacted to Rantour. Every time he thought about the cave, his fear of Rantour returned with the same full force.

Chapter Four
Reflecting on Fear

Since Barrabou's birth, his grandfather, Morinour, frequently visited Rantour's and Aleyma's pride. His reason, of course, was to spend time with Barrabou and guide the youngster in the ways of the lion. Occasionally, Morinour would also take Barrabou to visit his pride.

From visiting with his grandfather and being with his father, Barrabou saw that the two kings were quite different in their approaches. They seemed almost opposites: Rantour "ruled with an iron paw"; Morinour led with trust and respect. Barrabou also sensed that both father and son knew they were at opposite poles but loved and respected each other enough to never confront each other.

When it seemed appropriate to Morinour, he would talk with Barrabou about living life as he saw and experienced it. He hoped that some of his views would balance Rantour's influence on Barrabou. But Morinour was very careful not to speak negatively about Rantour where he knew they disagreed. Above all, he did not want to undermine the relationship between Barrabou and his father. Morinour's only desire was to give Barrabou alternate ways of looking at how to accomplish things, so Barrabou could choose for himself how to act.

Having observed Barrabou often, Morinour knew he was a watcher and a thinker, so Morinour would wait for Barrabou to approach him with a question to start their conversations about life and how to act. How Morinour cherished the dialogues he and his bright young grandson engaged in! These often took place as the two strolled in the high grass a few kilometers outside the pride's village. Several weeks after Barrabou's encounter at the cave with his father, a significant dialogue began during one of these walks.

Barrabou described to his grandfather the still troubling experience with his father. He vividly described how Rantour's anger and ferociousness caused him to freeze and how anxious it made him. He told his grandfather that every time he thought about the cave, he became frightened all over again. And that as much as he used to enjoy going to the coolness of the cave to play, he had not been back since Rantour's rage. Barrabou confided to his grandfather that since that experience, he was afraid of his father, even though he dearly loved him.

When he finished, instead of asking Morinour a question, as he usually did, Barrabou waited for Morinour to respond.

Morinour thought for a moment and said, "Well, Barrabou, let's look at what happened at the cave. What did your father do that made you afraid?"

Immediately, Barrabou replied, "He cowered over me, and snorted, and . . . and yelled at me as he spoke. And when he was done, he roared ferociously and stomped away as if in triumph over a lesser lion he had just defeated."

"And this made you afraid?" Morinour asked.

"Yes, Grandpapa, oh yes! I still am whenever I think about it," Barrabou said. "Even now, I get anxious and fearful just thinking about it."

"And why do you think your father chose to talk to you that way, Barrabou?" Morinour asked.

Barrabou pondered and then replied, "Maybe Father was trying to make his point by example. I know he loves me, but I have seen him act ferociously in the pride with other lions. My asking about his different behaviors in the pride and at home started this whole thing."

"You may be right, Barrabou," Morinour said. "Your father might have been showing you the aggressiveness he uses to intimidate the other lions and how he controls them to maintain his unquestioned authority. And he makes this point further by roaring the last time for emphasis as he walks away."

Morinour continued, "I am sure your father approached you the way he did because he loves you so much, and he wanted you to understand what has made him successful. He wanted to show you his ways so you can use them for your success."

"That makes sense to me, Grandpapa. Just talking about this with you makes me feel better," Barrabou said.

"But Grandpapa," Barrabou continued, "I don't like being made to feel afraid, and I don't like having to be on my guard all the time or making others feel that way."

Morinour raised his eyebrows at this comment, showing his surprise at Barrabou's understanding and maturity. Before he spoke again, he thought to himself, "This young grandson of mine is truly an exceptional young lion with self-awareness and the ability to express his feelings so clearly." He said, "Barrabou, let's chat about that another time soon. I have some thoughts for you. But it is getting late, and we don't want to be caught out here alone in the high grass when the hyenas begin their prowl for dinner."

They returned to the pride village just before dusk. For the first time in weeks, Barrabou felt better about his father, Rantour. His grandfather had helped him explore his fear, and Barrabou felt more settled and accepting of it. They met Rantour as they were all approaching the family den.

Barrabou looked up at his father. With an unusual spring in his voice, he said, "Hi Dad, how was your day?" To his surprise, Rantour responded with a smile and began sharing happenings of the day. Barrabou felt that he and his father were rekindling their rapport. But Barrabou also knew he had just experienced his first significant Lesson.

After all this, Barrabou sought out Lucy to tell her everything that had happened with his father and his discussion with his grandfather. Lucy listened wide-eyed. When Barrabou finished, she said, "Barrabou, that was quite a time you had. I am sure there was a purpose to all of what happened, including your talk with Morinour."

That night, almost dozing off to sleep in his cozy corner of the den, Barrabou played back the discussion with Morinour earlier that day and his exchange to with father later that evening. He closed his eyes and, in his head, wrote his first Spirit of the Lion Lesson, then tucked it away and fell into a peaceful sleep.

Spirit of the Lion
<u>Lesson One</u>

Understand Fear, But Do Not Be Fearful

• It is healthy and valuable to understand fear.

• In relationships, being afraid is self-destructive.

• Fear increases your anxiety and dulls your senses. It inhibits observing, listening, and thinking clearly.

• Fear paralyzes. It ruins the trust in relationships and causes disconnects with others. It can create suspicion and isolation.

• Fear will rob you of the ability to act.

• Recognize and work through your fears as quickly as possible, so you can function with all your capabilities and stay connected with others in mutually supportive and respectful relationships.

Lucy was right—there was a purpose.

Chapter Five

It's Okay to Flinch

It was several weeks since Morinour had last seen Barrabou. Morinour now made the journey across the plains again to visit his grandson. He purposely took the trip at a leisurely pace to think about the discussion he would have with his grandson.

Morinour traveled several days and nights to be waiting at the den when Barrabou awoke. Even though Morinour had walked most of the last night, he arrived early enough to sleep for a couple of hours.

He lay in the early morning sun as Barrabou, yawning and still not quite awake, approached him from the den. Barrabou was surprised but pleased to see his grandfather.

"Good morning, Grandpapa," Barrabou said lovingly. "It is good to see you." He sat down close to Morinour.

"Good morning, my Grandson," Morinour replied with a smile. "I have come to visit with you." Barrabou knew that most of Morinour's visits to their pride were to be with him, but he was always glad to hear his grandfather say so.

"Barrabou," Morinour said, "do you remember our talk in the high grass a few weeks ago?"

"Of course, I do," Barrabou answered. "Our talk helped me very much. It helped me to think about and deal with my fear about father."

"Well, I too have been thinking about that. I wanted to continue our discussion and take up where we left off," Morinour said. "Would you come to walk with me to the river?"

"Barrabou nodded and said, "Of course, Grandpapa."

In contrast to the pride's village area of low brown grass and scrawny bushes, the river was a lush oasis of high trees and deep green vegetation. Barrabou spent many hours at the river. The air had a soft mist from the water splashing off the many rocks in its path. The constant gurgling of the water over the stones soothed Barrabou and made him calm. It was tranquil here, an excellent place to talk, and Barrabou looked forward to it.

Morinour and Barrabou stretched out on the cool earth of the river-bank.

"Barrabou," Morinour started, "when we talked in the high grass, you expressed not liking the feeling of being afraid, not wanting to have to be on your guard, or not making others feel that way."

"Yes, Grandpapa, I recall telling you those things. I still feel that way," Barrabou said.

"I have been thinking about that," Morinour said. "What you did was to reflect to your father the emotions he projected to you. He purposely created fear, and he wanted you to internalize that so he could dominate the situation. It is a technique to control others. It means 'control by me over others.'"

Morinour continued, "This technique is focused only on 'me,' what I want, at the expense of the feelings and interest of others."

"This is one way to be king. But, as you said, it made you very uncomfortable. Others respond to this technique, as you did, but it does not make for pleasant or good relationships. It does just the opposite. It is not trusting or caring, or respectful, and it will not last long. Others resent this treatment. The 'controller' must continually reinforce his position by repeatedly creating a situation of fear or confusion so that he can maintain that control."

Barrabou's eyes widened as Morinour continued. "It takes a lot of energy to 'be in control' of others. It focuses on being negative and manipulating others solely for what 'I' want. I have never liked the style—it breeds perpetual anxiety and stress for everyone involved."

Morinour paused and concluded, "But, strangely, it can work—at a price though. It destroys trust among everyone and prevents the group from working together."

Barrabou had been listening with his ears wide open. He understood the logic of what Morinour had said and periodically nodded to show his understanding.

"In my pride," Morinour said, "we had a lion who acted by trying to control other lions all the time. He would do things that angered the other lions, but he was not strong enough to make the others bow down to him. He would try to boss other lions and, when that didn't work, he would try to take credit for what others had done. He was really 'Me First', and everyone felt it. But one day, he had an experience that made him think twice about continuing that way."

Barrabou listened intently. "What was it?"

"One evening," his grandfather said, "several of us were patrolling the pride perimeter against predators." Even with a bright moon, it was an unusually dark night. Out of nowhere, a huge bull elephant came out of the darkness and charged the village right where this lion was. He knew it was his responsibility to protect the area he was patrolling and scare the elephant back and away from the pride. But the elephant was so large and aggressive that he had trouble scaring the huge beast. He roared for help, but none of us came to his aid. Instead, we formed a secondary line between him and the village to confront the elephant if he got past the lion and came closer to the village."

"What happened?" asked Barrabou.

"We watched as the elephant toyed with the lion for a while. And then it got serious. The elephant was not playing any more. With his trunk, that huge beast began to swat with large arcs at the lion. He caught the lion with one stroke squarely in the torso and knocked the wind out of him. The blow carried the lion several yards into the air. He landed with a heavy thud on the hard ground.

"The lion lay on his side trying to recover as we saw the elephant rush over and start to raise his leg directly over the lion in an attempt to crush in his side. When we realized how serious this was, we all rushed the elephant. We were able to confuse the elephant enough to distract him from the downed lion. We nipped at the elephant's legs so that he gave up on trying to hurt the lion further. The elephant got tired of all of us pestering him and finally lost interest. He turned back away from the pride and disappeared into the night."

"Wow!" said Barrabou.

His grandfather continued "The lion lay on the ground disoriented and exhausted. We all went over to him to make sure he was not seriously injured, and then without a word, we left him there. "

"From what happened, I think it was obvious to that lion that none of us appreciated his attempt to be overbearing and controlling in the pride and that depending on us would mean he needed to act as a team member, and not just for himself. He understood. Later, he came over to each of us and thanked us for saving him. Since then, he has been a 'we first' lion, and we all appreciate him more."

When Morinour concluded, Barrabou said, "I understand, Grandpapa. I don't like that 'Me First' attitude, and I see now how it can backfire, too."

Morinour continued the discussion. "The alternative is learning to manage myself. I can choose to focus on how I act instead of trying to control others. I can manage my attitude and focus on joining with others to support them and what is best for all of us. I like this style because it includes what I want and what I desire as a member of our group but not at the expense of others. It promotes trust and respect, and appreciation among all of us. This philosophy is 'We First.' Very quickly, that lion learned how valuable 'We First' is."

Again, Barrabou nodded his understanding, but this time with a smile. "I like that!" he said.

Morinour was glad to see Barrabou's reaction. He paused and then added, almost in a whisper, so Barrabou had to lean forward to hear him, "Barrabou, if you are 'we'-focused, it is okay to flinch."

"We all have vulnerabilities and feel alone sometimes. If you take the risk to show this to others, they will identify with it and will appreciate that you have trusted them enough to show your weaknesses and concerns."

Morinour winked at Barrabou and repeated, "Sometimes, in the right circumstances, which you can create, Barrabou, it is okay to flinch."

Barrabou looked at his grandfather and said, "So, Grandpapa, I can choose to either act 'for me' or act 'for we.' I think I choose 'We First.'" They both laughed.

"That is a good way to remember it, Barrabou. I like that, too!" Morinour said.

They rose, stretched, and walked to the edge of the river for a cool drink before heading back to the pride.

As they walked, Barrabou knew this was a precious lesson. It reminded him of how he and Lucy acted together, always considering the other first. Thinking of Lucy made him smile. It was a comforting feeling.

Considering this discussion, Barrabou committed to memory his second Spirit of the Lion Lesson and wrote it down.

Spirit of the Lion Lesson
Lesson Two

"We First" Instead of "Me First"

- To encourage trust and respect so that we can do good things together, each of us must adopt a "We First" attitude.

- If any of us focuses on "Me First", we will try to control and dominate each other. This emphasis will create distrust and prevent us from caring for and respecting each other. We will be unable to move forward and make progress together. We will not survive.

- "We First" is non-threatening. It is easy to be honest with each other. We can share more openly and develop enough trust to show our vulnerabilities. With "We First," we can make progress together because we act in ways that are best for the group.

- With a "We First" attitude, it is natural to project caring and concern for others. When we do, others reflect that back to us. This reflection creates a positive atmosphere and excitement to work together. It has a much more lasting effect than "Me First."

- There is a big difference in outcomes between "Me First" and "We First":

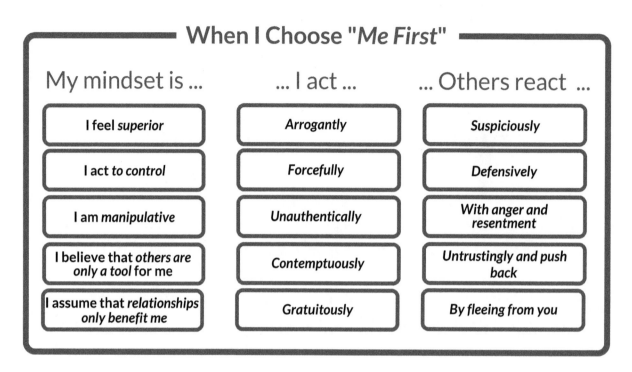

When I Choose "*Me First*"

My mindset is ...	... I act ...	... Others react ...
I feel *superior*	*Arrogantly*	*Suspiciously*
I act *to control*	*Forcefully*	*Defensively*
I am *manipulative*	*Unauthentically*	*With anger and resentment*
I believe that *others are only a tool* for me	*Contemptuously*	*Untrustingly and push back*
I assume that *relationships only benefit me*	*Gratuitously*	*By fleeing from you*

OR

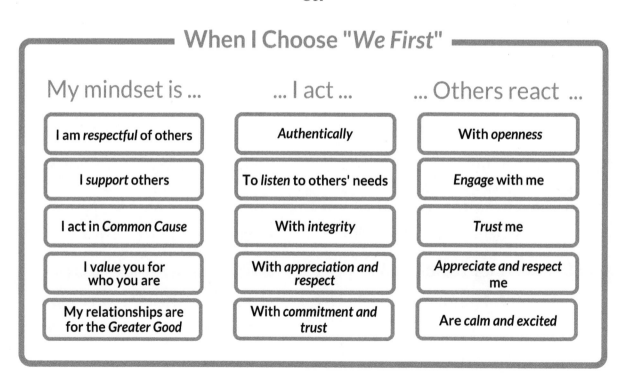

When I Choose "*We First*"

My mindset is ...	... I act ...	... Others react ...
I am *respectful* of others	*Authentically*	With *openness*
I *support* others	To *listen* to others' needs	*Engage* with me
I act in *Common Cause*	With *integrity*	*Trust* me
I *value* you for who you are	With *appreciation and respect*	*Appreciate and respect* me
My relationships are for the *Greater Good*	With *commitment and trust*	Are *calm and excited*

Chapter Six
The Destructiveness of Competing

Barrabou continued to grow. He knew that it would be time for him to leave his parents' pride to form his own by his second or third birthday.

He repeated to himself the principles he would use to successfully serve as King when he had his own pride. He had already internalized how to deal with his fears and how to stay focused on "we" for the greater good of the group instead of "me" focused just on himself.

He was about to experience another very personal lesson.

It started one day while Barrabou was watching some of the older lions playing in a field just outside the pride village. Lucy and some other young female lions were on the sidelines watching the game, too.

Barrabou knew all these lions and was constantly impressed by their agility and athleticism. When he saw them, he always thought about what great protectors of the pride each of them would become.

They were wrestling with a sizeable semi-round rock, playing keep it away from each other. They friskily growled as each would get control of the rock and try to keep it to himself, only to have another's paw slip in and take it away.

Since it looked like so much fun, Barrabou joined in the fray. The group continued playing, enjoying the game. Each lion tried to outmaneuver and outwit the other to keep control of the rock.

Suddenly, without warning, one of the older lions in the game lunged in the direction of Barrabou and another lion standing next to him. Out of the corner of his eye, Barrabou saw the lion attack and was able to dodge out of his way just enough that the lion's hindquarter pushed Barrabou out of danger of the attack. Barrabou was knocked on his side. He quickly recovered and scampered out of striking distance, never taking his eyes off the enraged attacker. Barrabou instinctively ran to Lucy to get her out of the way and protect her.

The lion who had been standing next to Barrabou wasn't so lucky. The attacking lion's lunge focused on him. A wide-open mouth of glistening teeth hit him. Barrabou and the others watched in horror as the attacker's teeth sunk solidly into the other lion's shoulder. When the attacker knew he had made a successful strike and had a good grip on the shoulder, he furiously shook his head, further taking his victim under control.

The attacked lion did a quick somersault and was able to wriggle free but, in doing so, further injured his shoulder. The attacker backed away and made a second strike. The victim roared in great pain as the strike found its mark into the open wound. The attacker again backed off, preparing for a final hit on the shoulder. Seeing this, the wounded lion sprang backward and limped away and out of range of the third attack as quickly as he could.

The attacker stood panting heavily. He did not explain what had happened. It appeared that the game had gotten out of hand for him, and he had lashed out. After a short time, he settled down and trotted away into the bush.

All this took only a few moments, but it was devastating to the players and onlookers. Most of the players scattered quickly to the far ends of the village to hide out of harm's way and any further outburst from the attacking lion.

The hurt lion's shoulder was bleeding profusely. Several of the other lions ran to the river to wet their paws with mud. They returned to cover the injured lion's wound with the wet soil to salve the pain and help stop the bleeding. But the other lions knew that he had sustained a severe injury.

Barrabou was scared and shaken by what had happened. Lucy was horrified. Lucy saw from Barrabou's expression that he was as rattled by the situation as she. Together, they sped away from the field to the cave to be alone.

Barrabou could hear his heart beating loudly and swiftly from the adrenaline rush of the experience. It sapped his energy, and as he lay in the protective shadow of the cave, he calmed down and fell asleep. Lucy lay beside him, trying to relax, and watched him sleep. She kept dozing off, also exhausted from the ordeal.

Barrabou dreamed about what had just occurred.

In his dream, it was three weeks after the incident. The attacked lion's injury had healed, but he now had a permanent limp where his leg connected to the shoulder that had sustained the damage. The limp was obvious when he ran. He and several other lions were grazing in the field just before dusk, involved in their chatter. They failed to see a band of hyenas quietly approaching them on the prowl for food.

The hyenas' scent finally hit the lions, and they ran in all directions to escape. The hyenas watched for a brief second to see which of the lions to converge on. They saw the one lion limping away, trying to gain speed. Looking at each other knowingly, the hyenas all ran toward the limping lion. It took just a few seconds for them to catch up to him and take him down. In no time, it was over. They dragged his body away over the horizon to a safe place to feast.

Barrabou awoke with a start, sweating profusely. It took him a moment to realize where he was and that what he had just seen was only a dream. But the impression lasted.

Lucy jumped when Barrabou abruptly awoke and said, "Barrabou, are you okay?" He told her about his dream and how earlier in the day, a playful game had turned into serious competition. Then, in his dream, the result was the downfall and then death of one of their own. Had this actually happened, he said, their internal competition would have caused the pride to lose one of their potentially strongest protectors.

Barrabou made a mental note to himself and said to Lucy, "When I am the king of my pride, I will warn us all about the divisiveness of competing among ourselves. Instead of using our skills to compete, I will help us to learn the unique value that each of us can bring to help us all in the pride. Using all of what we have for our common purpose will help us respect and appreciate each other. It will strengthen our common bonds."

He then wrote his third Spirit of the Lion Lesson.

Spirit of the Lion Lesson
Lesson Three

We Must Contribute for the Benefit of All and Not Compete Among Ourselves
Internal Competition Is Destructive

- Competing among ourselves can be unconscious, and it can be insidious. It destroys the environment we need to work together for our common purpose.

- When we compete, we are choosing not to support each other. Someone will "win," and someone will "lose." In truth, we will all lose because we will fail to see the unique value that each of us can contribute to satisfy our common needs and to reach our group's shared goals.

- Internal competition breeds mistrust and suspicion of others. Trust and positive, appreciative, and respectful relationships foster harmony, accomplishment, and satisfaction for all.

- Relying on or allowing internal competition to be the foundation to reach positive ends is inconsistent and will not work. We cannot use a negative means and expect to have a positive outcome.

Lucy added, "Valuable competition is one competing with oneself to be the best he or she can be. This focus is non-offensive to others and can help contribute to the group in a meaningful way."

Barrabou smiled at Lucy and said, "That's a great thought! I like that," and he gave her a gentle lick on the face.

Chapter Seven
For the Good of Us All

As one of the strongest and largest lionesses in the pride, and as the Queen of the pride, Aleyma led the hunt for the pride's food. On one such search, Barrabou observed a most significant occurrence.

The hunting party had a well-worked-out strategy for stalking prey. The lionesses would slowly and quietly move as a group, spreading out over a large area. Aleyma would put herself in the center of the hunting party. While all held their positions, they would survey the area and locate a small grouping of animals. The lionesses on the group's wings would identify a specific animal to attack and try to spook it to run toward the center where Aleyma was waiting.

Aleyma would crouch low to the ground closely tracking the prey with her eyes. She would follow the target back and forth across the hunting area as the other lionesses taunted it. When she sensed that moment when the animal was dazed and confused, she would strike for the kill.

On this night, the lioness hunting party had been out for several hours without any luck. They had almost given up to return to the pride empty-handed. Their success was crucial because the pride had not eaten well for a while. They had been barely subsisting on what they could scavenge.

But now, the lionesses sensed and then heard a small group of plains buffalo slowly heading toward them. Each of the lionesses instinctively stopped and crouched in the high grass, waiting for the patter of hooves to get louder.

One of the younger lionesses on Aleyma's left flank raised her head slightly to see the seven buffalo coming closer. A large buffalo lagged somewhat behind the rest, lazily stopping now and then to graze. The hunting party went into action. Using the strategy they had successfully employed before, they isolated this lone buffalo and ran it to ground from the left flank directly into Aleyma's path.

Aleyma easily pounced on the startled buffalo and quickly overcame it.

Triumph!

As was their custom, the lioness who made the kill would return to the pride to announce the success. The other lionesses would stay to protect the carcass until the pride arrived to feast.

Immediately after the kill, Aleyma headed toward the pride to announce the success and lead the pride to the downed buffalo. On hearing the news, the entire pride gathered to follow Aleyma back. They arrived to see the hunting party formed in a wide circle around the untouched animal, guarding their catch. None had dared to even nibble at the buffalo. It was well known that only the King of the pride could start the feeding and satisfy himself first. If any other lion started before him, he would get a terrible thrashing by the king.

The pride members joined the circle with the lionesses around the buffalo. Barrabou and Lucy stood at the circle's perimeter with the other cubs. Shortly after they assembled, King Rantour made his entrance. He pranced into the center of the ring. With one paw on the downed carcass, he looked at each of the lions and roared to signify that he was the king and that he, and only he, would eat. The rest of the pride scattered to leave Rantour to feast by himself.

As Rantour ate, the scent of the food grew stronger and stronger, luring some of the pride closer to him. He watched them carefully, and each time they grew near, Rantour swatted at them and roared to make them retreat. Rantour ate by himself with great zeal. When he was finally satiated, he turned and moved away from the buffalo carcass and slowly lumbered off into the nearby brush to lay down. He fell into a deep sleep, his stomach fuller than it had been in months.

Rantour leaving the kill was the signal that the rest of the strong male lions could safely feed. The lionesses, cubs, and elders, including Barrabou and Lucy, waited at a safe distance. They watched the males approach the buffalo in unison. Each eyed the other as if to decide when to spring to get the first mouthful. As they came, cautiously watching each other, they moved to get the best share of the feast. They nipped at each other's legs and shoulders and roared, jockeying for the best feeding spot.

Standing shoulder-to-shoulder, the lions pulled at the meat in a fierce whirl of motion. If one thought he could gain a better position, he would create a small skirmish and try to jostle another lion out of his way.

Barrabou held his position several yards away. As hungry as he was, he held back, afraid to approach too closely and get his legs and shoulders nipped. Like Barrabou, the rest of the pride watched the lions devour the catch.

It was over in no more than ten minutes. The lions had finished feeding. But to Barrabou's dismay, they had eaten almost the entire buffalo. Then they followed Rantour's example. Each strolled away to find a comfortable place to doze off.

When the lions were well away from the feeding area, the lionesses, cubs, and elders approached what was left of the buffalo. They picked at what they could. Little remained for them to eat. Some were able to salvage meager bits, but most of them went hungry. Barrabou was able to snag a tiny piece of gristle he shared with Lucy, but he too got almost nothing to eat.

It was almost sunrise. Barrabou made his way slowly back to the pride village with the others. He was disheartened and went to bed very hungry.

When he awoke, Barrabou was hungrier still. He got up and walked to the river. He ate some leaves and grass and then drank from the river to fill his belly, but all this did little to ease his hunger.

Barrabou was still tired from the last night's activity. Instead of joining to play with the other cubs, he rested at the riverbank. He pondered what had happened the night before and began to talk to himself about it.

He reasoned that it made no sense to him for the king and the strong lions to eat first and leave nothing for the rest of the pride. As his stomach growled, he even got a little angry about that. He mused further. "When I am King of my pride, I will start a discussion among all of us about food and survival. We will reach an agreement on how we will feed to take care of all of us.

"Instead of the "Me First" mentality I witnessed last night with the king and lions gorging themselves at the expense of no food for others, I will suggest that we feed in a more logical fashion that serves us more effectively. I will beckon everyone to consider that we first provide for our cubs and help them to eat. Why? Our healthy cubs will ensure that we survive and carry on. Our cubs are our future.

"Then, I will suggest that we make way for our lionesses to eat. They must stay healthy to nurse and care for our cubs. They are also our hunters and need their strength to gather food for us.

"Next, I will say that we should honor our elders and ask them to feed. We have much to learn from them about how they have prospered and survived. And, if not for them, none of us would be here. They are our history.

"And then, I will suggest that the lions feast in their pecking order, but that this be done quietly and without hurting each other. They are our protectors and the future fathers of our species. We need them healthy too.

"Lastly, I will ask that they leave some food for me, their king. Only after all the pride is fed shall I feed."

Barrabou smiled to himself, satisfied. This plan made sense to him. It would ensure the common focus of the pride—what the pride needed to survive and carry on—and fulfill the needs of all.

He summarized these thoughts by vocalizing another Spirit of the Lion Lesson. It would be his last Lesson before he prepared to leave his parent's pride to go out on his own. He knew his time to leave was near.

Spirit of the Lion Lesson
Lesson Four

Focus for Common Purpose and Act on That Basis
Value What Each Group Member Brings to Our Common Purpose

- If we can define and agree on our group's common purpose and focus, we will work better together in a common cause for results and aim for what is best for all of us.

- As each of us commits to fulfilling our common purpose, we will identify and resolve issues effectively.

- We will better empathize with each other and respect and appreciate what value each of us can contribute to fulfilling our shared objectives and goals.

Barrabou knew Lucy would be proud of his insights when he described them to her.

Chapter Eight
Moving On

A month had passed since that momentous hunt. Barrabou, now two-and-a-half years old, found himself feeling more and more uncomfortable being in the pride. And he knew why. It was time for him to move on, to leave and form his own pride.

In the last three months, Barrabou had become increasingly comfortable voicing his opinions openly to other young lions and adults as well. While he was always respectful of others, he would bring his strong ideas into conversations, and he was not afraid to debate topics with others. When he disagreed, he had a sound reason for his position, and he defended himself in conversations.

He was quietly proud that he stood up for what he believed. He knew he had come of age as a young adult, and he was ready to venture out independently. He also felt more and more unsettled by how his father ruled autocratically in the pride.

He decided that he would prepare for his departure from the pride and then tell his parents. With plans to leave forming in his head, Barrabou became very conscious of his surroundings—the pride village, the cave, and especially the riverbank. As he walked around, he thought about the good times and trying times with his family and friends in the pride.

He found he was drawn back to the cave and the river frequently, each time recalling all he had experienced and reflected on in the past two years.

He thought about trailing Rantour around the pride as a youngster, his talks with Morinour on every subject imaginable, and, of course, his discussions with Lucy.

Soon, the day came when Barrabou was ready to leave. Morinour had arrived to visit the family, and Barrabou knew it was time to announce his departure.

In midafternoon, with the family gathered resting near the den, Barrabou addressed them all.

"Mom, Dad, Grandpapa," he began confidently, "I have decided it is time for me to leave the pride." As he spoke, Barrabou looked at his sisters, his parents, and Morinour.

"You know I love you all very much. You are everything to me. But I also know that I must leave to begin my own life away from the pride. It is time for me to go, and I am comfortable doing that."

Everyone in the family listened to Barrabou but said nothing. They, too, had sensed for several weeks that this was coming.

Barrabou continued. "I will miss you all every day, and once I am settled, I will come back to visit, but it is time to go. It is time."

Rantour then said, "Barrabou, my son, we are all very proud of you. We know you must go, but you know that we are all here to help you whenever you call." Aleyma and Morinour looked at each other and then at Barrabou, nodding their support.

Morinour added, "Yes, my grandson, call me, and I will be there." He smiled his familiar smile of love and affection that always comforted Barrabou.

Barrabou looked once more from one face to the other and said, "Thank you all. Thank you for everything you have done for me."

In turn, he approached each of them: First, Aleyma, then each of his sisters, then Rantour, and finally Morinour. He licked each of them gently on the cheek. And then, slowly, he walked off in the direction of the river.

Barrabou spent his last evening in the pride by the river. For an hour, he lay calmly on the bank with his eyes closed, listening to the running river. He reviewed all the lessons he had learned. These would be the foundation for how he would start his pride, how he would relate to the other lions, and how he hoped the new pride would function for the best results.

In his mind, he summarized the Spirit of the Lion Lessons he had memorized.

- Understand Fear, But Do Not Be Fearful
- Be "We First" Instead of "Me First"

- We Must Contribute for the Benefit of All

- Not Compete Among Ourselves

- Internal Competition Is Destructive

- Focus for Common Purpose and Act on That Basis

- Value What Each Group Member Brings to Our Common Purpose

Barrabou tucked these away in his head so he could recall them at a moment's notice. He knew that if he stayed conscious of these principles and actively used them, they would serve him and his new pride well.

Blinking his eyes several times, Barrabou took a deep breath, exhaled peacefully, and rose from the riverbank. He looked around slowly one more time to absorb this wonderful place of his upbringing, this place he loved so much. Then he turned and left.

But he had one more stop to make. He went to visit Lucy and told her of his plan to leave. Although he hinted at her coming with him, he did not suggest it fearing she would say no to going with him. So, Barrabou just gently licked the side of her face and said goodbye.

He trotted off in the direction of the plains grasses. The further he moved away from the pride, the faster he ran. Had you seen him running through the grass, you would have smiled to see him jumping straight up in the air every so often and hearing him laugh out loud as he ran.

He was happy—with a solid grounding. Except for missing Lucy, he felt the excitement and exhilaration to start on his own independent life.

As he ran, he became aware of approaching footfalls behind him. He turned and saw Lucy running as fast as she could to catch up with him. With a wide grin on his face, he stopped and waited for her.

Barrabou could not recall ever being so happy.

Discussion Guide

The Lion Who Flinched

The Cub Who Would Be King

Jed Selter

Discussion Guide
Introduction

This book consists of a story and this supplemental guide, which will give adults and adolescents a road map to help apply the principles described in the story.

Most chapters in the story conclude with a "Spirit of the Lion Lesson" to reiterate the central premise of that chapter.

In this guide, each "Lesson" is repeated from the book, followed by a brief "Introspection" worksheet for adults to use in applying the Lesson to themselves.

Each Introspection is followed by a "Dialogue with Cubs" for parents, guardians, teachers, and other youth leaders to engage adolescents in discussions about the subject of the chapter.

By reading this book to or with adolescents and using the guide, I hope that adults can open dialogues with young adults so they, too, can internalize tools to live with grace and peace of mind.

Guide for Chapters 1-4
About Fear

This section of the Guide, Spirit of the Lion Lesson One—About Fear, relates to Chapters One through Four of the story. It includes the Introspection Worksheet for Adults and the Dialogue with Cubs Worksheet.

Spirit of the Lion – Lesson One
Understand Fear, but Do Not Be Fearful

- It is healthy and valuable to understand fear.

- In relationships, being fearful is self-destructive.

- Fear will increase your anxiety and dull your senses. It inhibits hearing, listening, and thinking clearly.

- Fear paralyzes. It ruins the trust in relationships and causes disconnects with others. It can create suspicion and isolation.

- Fear will rob you of the ability to act.

- Recognize and work through your fears as quickly as possible, so you can function with all your capabilities and stay connected with others in mutually supportive and respectful relationships.

About Fear
Introspection Worksheet for Adults

The following exercise is intended for adults to practice becoming aware of and dealing with their fears. It will require a pen or pencil and paper.

- Think about something you are afraid of and write it down. (It can be anything: a situation, a responsibility, a relationship in your personal or professional life or fear of rejection or fear of failure.)

- How does this fear manifest itself in you? It is essential to identity and recognize how this fear affects you. Write down how this fear affects you (such as feeling confused, feeling angry, being agitated, sweating, muscle tenseness, headaches, or lack of self-confidence).

- List some reasons for this fear (such as insecurity or newness in a relationship, or lack of experience to deal with a situation).

- For each of the reasons above, describe reasonable actions you can take to change the course of the fear (such as opening up to a new relationship or reflecting on previous experiences that may relate to a new challenge).

• Test each action by taking that action and observing if it lessens the effects of the fear you described above.

• To ensure success, you may need to repeat the steps. Use this process to tackle other fears you may have.

• If this procedure is not successful, list new reasons and actions. Follow the process and your progress, ensuring that you are honest and truthful with yourself about the reasons and actions you describe and use.

Notes

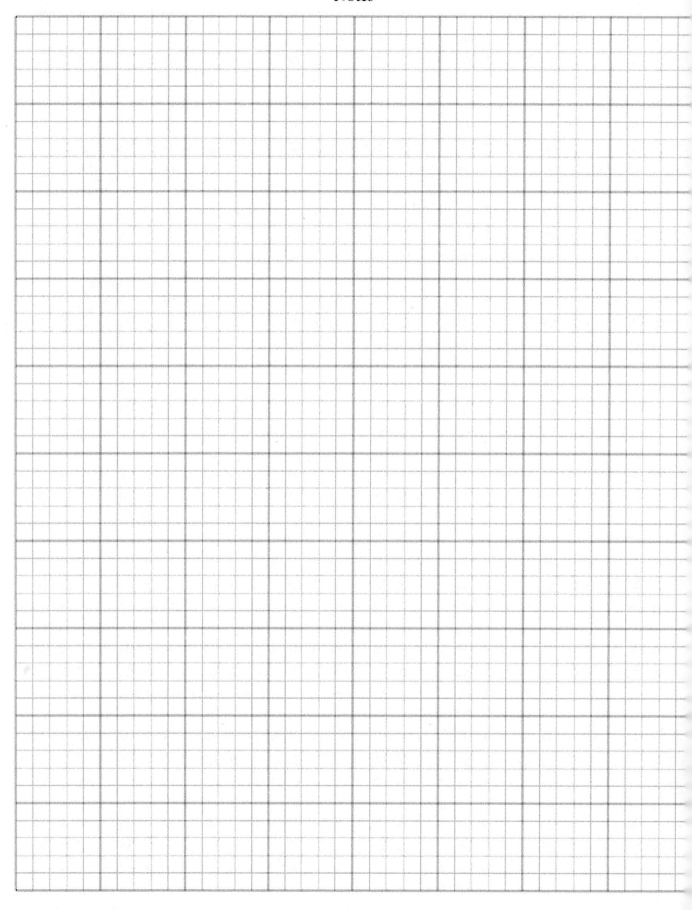

Notes

About Fear
Dialogue with Cubs

After completing the worksheet on the previous page, you may have some experience working through one of your fears. This may help you talk to your adolescents about fear and guide them through the process you used. Here is a suggestion for that sequence:

- Have your adolescents read (or read to them) Chapters One through Four of this book.

- Discuss the chapters with them.

- Describe to them in general terms a fear you have overcome.

- Ask them to describe something they are afraid of and how it makes them feel.

- Explore what actions they think they could take to eliminate making them feel that way.

- Follow through with them on the results of their taking actions to eliminate their negative feelings. Ask them if they are feeling less fearful.

- Suggest additional actions they can take to eliminate the negative feelings and the fear.

Guide for Chapter 5

"Me First", "We First"

This section of the Guide, Spirit of the Lion Lesson Two—Me First, We First, relates to Chapter Five of the story. It includes the Introspection Worksheet for Adults and the Dialogue with Cubs Worksheet.

I Choose "Me First" - Actions and Reactions (Graphic)

I Choose "We First" - Actions and Reactions (Graphic)

Spirit of the Lion – Lesson Two
"We First," Instead of "Me First"

- To develop trust and respect, so we can do good things together, each of us must adopt a "We First" attitude.

- If any of us focuses on "Me First," we will try to control and dominate each other. This emphasis will create distrust and prevent us from caring for and respecting each other. We will be unable to move forward and make progress together. We will not survive.

- "We First" is non-threatening. It is easier to be honest with each other. We can share more openly and develop enough trust to show our vulnerabilities. With "We First," we can make progress together, because we are all acting in ways that are best for the group.

- With a "We First" attitude, it is natural to project caring and concern for others. When we do, others reflect that back to us. This reflection creates a positive atmosphere and excitement to work together. It has a much more lasting effect than "Me First."

- There is a big difference in relationships and outcomes between ""Me First"" and "We First."

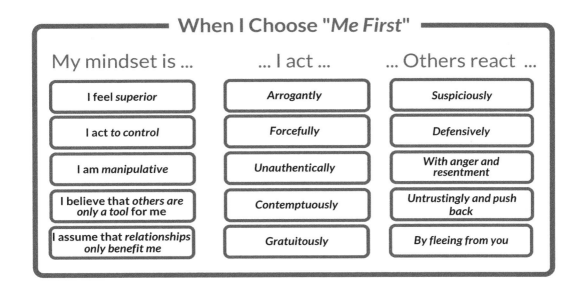

When I Choose "*Me First*"

My mindset is ...	... I act ...	... Others react ...
I feel *superior*	Arrogantly	Suspiciously
I act *to control*	Forcefully	Defensively
I am *manipulative*	Unauthentically	With anger and resentment
I believe that *others are only a tool* for me	Contemptuously	Untrustingly and push back
I assume that *relationships only benefit me*	Gratuitously	By fleeing from you

I Act: Consciously and unconsciously, everything I project to you will be defensive, "pushy" and forced.

You React: You will react by being wary of me. You will feel uneasy around me. You will not want to be around me, nor will you trust me.

OR

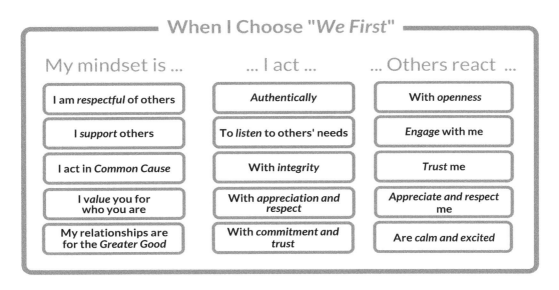

When I Choose "*We First*"

My mindset is ...	... I act ...	... Others react ...
I am *respectful* of others	Authentically	With *openness*
I *support* others	To *listen* to others' needs	*Engage* with me
I act in *Common Cause*	With *integrity*	*Trust* me
I *value* you for who you are	With *appreciation and respect*	*Appreciate and respect* me
My relationships are for the *Greater Good*	With *commitment and trust*	Are *calm and excited*

I Act: I will project my attitude to you of respect for and openness toward you. I will think and speak highly of you, and I will be supportive of you.

You React: You will be excited to collaborate with me. We will be able to focus on the common good we can accomplish together.

"Me First" or "We First"
Introspection

The following exercise is intended for adults to identify and work to improve a personal or professional relationship. It will require a pen or pencil and paper. Write down your responses to the following questions:

Think about an individual with whom you interact where an element of anxiety and tension may be limiting your relationship.

- What is the basis of the anxiety and tension? Is it due to "Me First" attitudes and behavior? On whose part? Yours? The other person's? Both of you?

- How could you act differently to eliminate the anxiety and increase positive connections with that person (focus on "We First" attitudes and behavior)?

- In response to the above questions, what specific actions are you willing to take to improve this relationship?

- After taking these actions to improve this relationship, can you see changes in the reactions to your actions?

- What are they?

- Is the relationship improving?

- What other additional actions can you take to continue to improve this relationship? Commit to taking these.

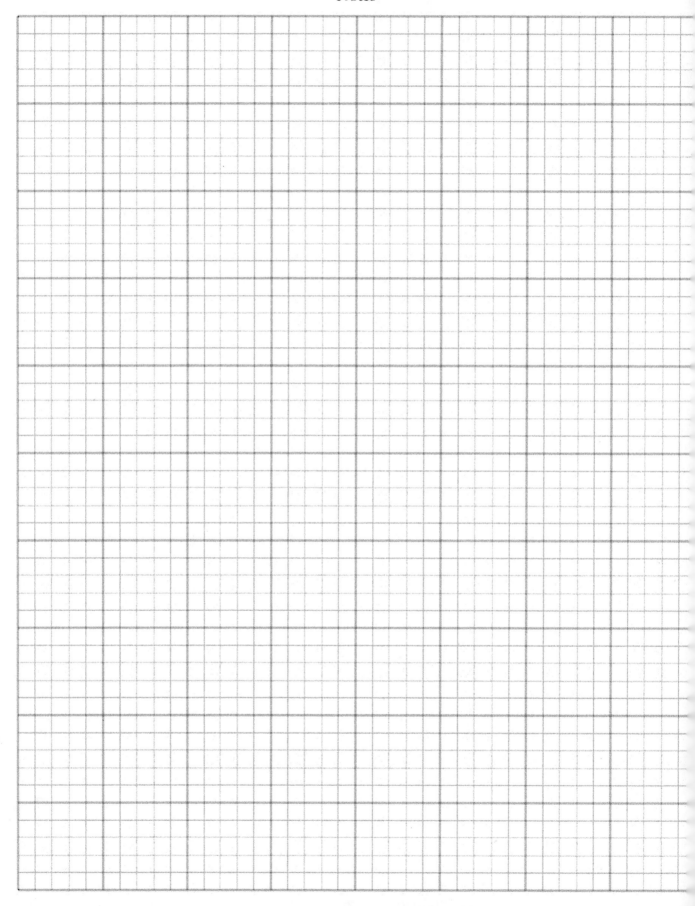

"Me First" or "We First"
Dialogue with Cubs

After completing the Introspection, so you have some experience with the process to improve a relationship, talk to the adolescents about this subject. Guide them through the process you used. Here is a suggestion for that sequence:

- Have them read (or read to them) Chapter Five of this book.

- Discuss the chapter with them.

- Describe to them in general terms the relationship improvements you accomplished using the process on the previous page.

- Ask them to describe a relationship with a peer that involves a high level of anxiety or stress.

- Explore what they and the other person may be doing which adds to the poor relationship.

- Discuss how this negative relationship makes them feel and how they think it makes others feel.

- Explore with them what actions they think they could take to improve the relationship.

- Ask them to commit to taking the actions which could improve the relationship, and when doing so, to observe if the other person acts more positively toward them.

- Ask them how the relationship now feels after these actions and how they think the others feel.

- Follow through with them on the results of this and discuss what more they can do to continue to improve the relationship.

Guide for Chapter 6
Competition

"Me First", "We First"

This section of the Guide, Spirit of the Lion Lesson Three—Internal Competition Is Destructive, relates to Chapter Six of the story.

We Must Contribute for the Benefit of All and Not Compete Among Ourselves.

It includes the Introspection Worksheet for Adults and the Dialogue with Cubs Worksheet.

Spirit of the Lion – Lesson Three

We Must Contribute for the Benefit of All and Not Compete Among Ourselves
Internal Competition Is Destructive

- Competing among ourselves can be unconscious, and it can be insidious. It destroys the environment we need to work together for our common purpose.

- When we compete, we are choosing not to support each other. Someone will "win," and someone will "lose." In truth, we will all lose because we will fail to see the unique value that each of us can contribute to satisfy our common needs and to reach our group's shared goals.

- Internal competition breeds mistrust and suspicion of others where trust and positive, appreciative, and respectful relationships are needed.

- Relying on or allowing internal competition to be the foundation to reach positive ends is inconsistent and will not work. We cannot use a negative means and expect to have positive outcomes.

Introspection - Competition

The following exercise is intended for adults to identify and work with to improve a competitive relationship. It will require a pen or pencil and paper. Write down your responses to the following questions:

Think about an individual with whom you are competing, either someone in your professional life, a peer, someone who reports to you or someone to whom you report, or in your personal life, such as with your spouse, a parent, or a sibling.

- Validate that you feel competition with this person by identifying and writing down the characteristics of your interaction. (e.g., mistrust, suspicion, withholding of information, argumentativeness, stress).

- Write down your view of the basis for feeling competitive with this person. (Was it something this person did or said? Was it something you did? How long ago?)

- If you are precipitating the competition, what are you doing? Or what did you do? How does/did this person react to what you do/did?

- If it is your view that the other person is precipitating this competitiveness, what is he/she doing, and how do you react to it?

- Think about and write down what negative impacts and

implications this competitive relationship has for you and the group you and this other person are members of.

- In your observations, how does this competition affect you?

- How does this competition affect the other members of the group?

- What could you do to reduce the competitiveness of this relationship? How would you approach and discuss this with the other person?

- Commit to taking the steps you described above to reduce this conflict and competition.

- Review how you feel about the actions you have taken and the reactions of the other person. Review what effects this change has for the members of the group.

- Discuss the positive aspects of the changes in the relationship with the person with whom you had been competing, so you can both work with the common goal of reducing your mutual competitiveness.

- Build on the positive aspects of your relationship to continue to strengthen it.

Notes

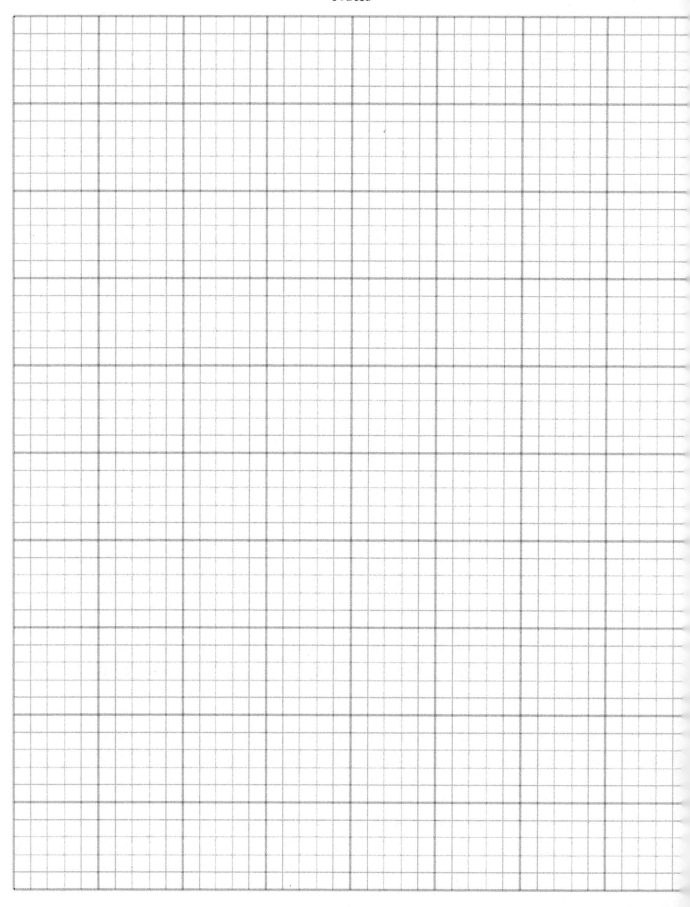

Notes

Dialogue with Cubs – Competition

After completing the Introspection on the previous page, so you have some experience with the process to improve a competitive relationship, talk to your young adults about this subject. Guide them through the process you used. Here is a suggestion for that sequence:

- Have them read (or read to them) Chapter Six of this book.

- Discuss the chapter with them.

- Describe to them improvements you have accomplished or are working on from relationships on the previous page.

- Ask them to describe a competitive relationship with a friend, peer, or family member.

- Explore with them what they and the other person may be doing that perpetuates this competitive relationship.

- Discuss with them how this negative relationship makes them feel, and how they think it makes the other person feel.

- Explore with them what actions they think they could take to improve the relationship.

- Ask them to commit to taking the actions which could improve the relationship, and when doing so, to observe if the other person acts more positively toward them.

- Ask them how the relationship now feels to them and how they think the other person feels.

- Ask them to tell you about the results of their thoughts or actions and discuss what more they can do to continue to improve the relationship.

- Ask them to talk with you about the positive aspects of this revitalized relationship and discuss ways with them to continue to strengthen the relationship.

Guide for Chapter 7
Focus for Common Purpose and Valuing Others

This section of the Guide, Spirit of the Lion Lesson Four—Common Purpose and Valuing Others, relates to Chapter Seven of the story.

Focus for Common Purpose and Act on That Basis. Value What Each Group Member Brings to Our Common Purpose.

It includes the Introspection Worksheet for Adults and the Dialogue with Cubs Worksheet.

Spirit of the Lion – Lesson Four
Focus for Common Purpose
and Valuing Others

Value What Each Group Member Brings to Our Common Purpose.

- If we can define and agree on our group's common purpose and focus, it will help us work together for common results and aim for what is best for all of us.

- Each of us committing to act toward fulfilling our common purpose will help us identify and resolve issues effectively.

- This behavior will help each of us empathize with each other and respect and appreciate what value each of us can contribute to fulfill our shared objectives and goals.

Introspection
Focus for Common Purpose
and Valuing Others

The following exercise is intended for adults to identify and help them focus on a common purpose in a professional or social group. It will require a pen or pencil and paper. Write down your responses to the following:

Identify and write down the name of a professional or social group of which you are a member.

- Does this group have a stated common purpose? Has it been discussed and agreed to by all in the group? If so, good. If not, start the dialogue for a common purpose to be defined and agreed upon.

- Think about the value that each member of the group brings to the group and to its common purpose. Write these down.

- Write down your view of what you believe you bring to the group.

- Suggest (and help start) dialogue in the group about what value each person brings to the group. Start by example and enunciate what you believe another member of the group brings to the group.

• Suggest the following exercise to start this dialogue:

• Have the group name a facilitator from within the group to lead this exercise. (The facilitator will lead the rest of this exercise.)

• Have each member of the group think about the value that each member brings to the group. Have them write down the name of every other group member on separate piece of paper or card.

• On each of these cards, have each member list five things they believe that group member contributes to the group.

• When this part is completed for each group member, have the cards given to the facilitator.

• The facilitator will group all the cards by each member's name and then read aloud to the group what the group believes each member brings to the group.

• The facilitator will then provide each member with the cards written about him or her to keep and think about.

• After the above exercise is completed, observe if you feel there is now a closer, more respectful aura among the group members.

• If you think there is, why do you think it exists now, and didn't before?

- If you think there is not, why not?

- Do you feel closer to others in the group?

- Suggest to the facilitator that the above questions be posed to the group and be discussed.

Notes

Notes

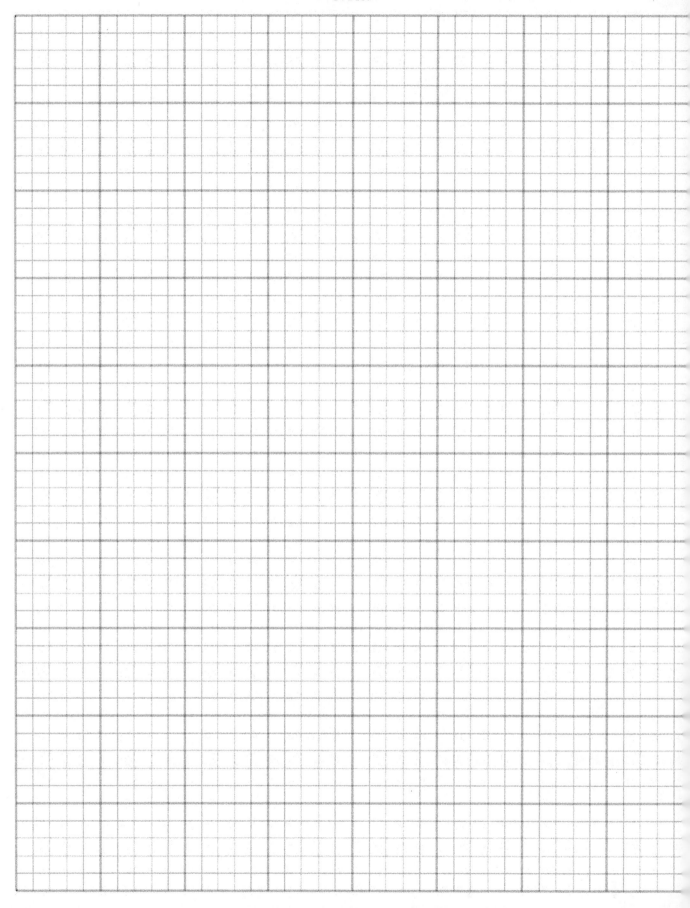

Dialogue with Cubs
Common Purpose and Valuing Others

After completing the Introspection on the previous page, so you have some experience with the process to increase common purpose and valuing others, talk to your adolescents about valuing and appreciating others. Guide them to consider the value each member brings to the group. Here is a suggestion for that sequence:

- Have them read (or read to them) Chapter Seven of this book.

- Discuss the chapter with them.

- Discuss with them what the concepts of common purpose and valuing others mean.

- Answer any questions they may have with examples from their social situations and your own but keep these at a level they will understand.

- Ask them to tell you about a group he or she is in and what that group's common purpose is. (Suggest a school class or project, a school club or sport, religious or social group or club he or she is a member of, such as Cubs Scouts, Brownies, or Camp Fire Girls).

- Ask them what value he or she thinks they bring to that group and discuss this with them. Reinforce their comments by telling him or her what you believe they bring to the group.

- Ask them to tell you the name of another person in the group, and what value or contribution they think that person brings to the group.

- Having thought about what value that person contributes to the group, ask them to describe how they feel about that person.

- If they feel better or happier about that person, ask them what changed and why they feel that way now.

- If they do not feel any different about that person, ask them why not.

- For either of the answers they provide, have a stimulating conversation about how relationships can improve when we focus on the positive things others bring to the group, and how thinking that way can improve relationships.

About the Author

Jed's heart-felt passion for people and his perspectives on relationships began when he was a teenager.

In high school and college, Jed worked with deaf and blind children and later organized and led a Boy Scout troop. After 5 years as an Officer/ Special Agent in the Air Force Office of Special Investigations, Jed pursued a management career in industry and retired as a mid-level executive in a Fortune 50 company.

Jed is founder and president of JS Associates, Inc. established to improve the lives of a broad spectrum of people and organizations.

Among his many professional accomplishments, Jed led national initiatives for industry with numerous government agencies and the White House to resolve policy issues affecting industry.

Throughout his career, Jed has been a keynote speaker at forums on the topics of motivation, leadership, and effective management.

Jed is a former 10-year volunteer with the American Red Cross and held several leadership positions in disaster relief and community support.

Jed is a co-founder, President and Executive Director of Caring Clowns International, an all-volunteer charitable nonprofit. Since its inception in 2002, their clowns have performed in over 35 developing countries and across the United States. The organization has provided hundreds of thousands of dollars to other nonprofits worldwide to help children in need. Please visit www.caringclownsinternational.org.

Jed holds a BS degree in Sociology/Psychology from Iowa State University. He is graduate of several Air Force and industry executive management programs.

To contact the author, please visit www.thelionwhoflinched.com.

CPSIA information can be obtained
at www.ICGtesting.com
Printed in the USA
BVHW021731120122
626005BV00007B/51

9 781952 685323